Broken Angels

Best wishes.
Mark McCrumm

This edition of Broken Angels published 2020
by MarkMiltonPublishing, Milton Lane, Wells BA5 2QS
mmiltonpublishing@outlook.com

ISBN 978-1-8380131-0-3

Broken Angels

A Tale of
Glastonbury Abbey

Beth Webb

Mark Hutchinson

Glossary

A monastic day was (and to some extent, still is,) split into periods for worship and prayer, rather than going by a clock. These are flexible depending on times of sunrise and sunset, etc, but very roughly speaking, a medieval monk would have attended:

Nocturns at about 2 a.m.

Matins or Lauds or Dawn Prayer at daybreak.

Prime or Early Morning Prayer at about 6 a.m.

Terce or Mid-Morning Prayer at about 8 a.m.

Sext or Midday Prayer at 11.30 am

None or Mid-Afternoon Prayer at about 2.30 p.m.

Vespers or Evening Prayer at about 6 p.m.

Compline or Night Prayer about 7 p.m.

Abbot – the man in charge of an abbey – like a modern CEO.

Almonry – a building where alms (charitable donations) and medical help were given to the poor.

Galilee steps – a flight of steps from the Galilee up to the nave of the church (see map).

Breeks – wool or linen short trousers.

Habit – a long, loose garment worn by both monks and nuns. The Benedictines usually wore a black habit with a leather belt.

Holy Chrism – holy oil used for sacraments such as anointing the sick.

Lammas-tide – August 1st, a holiday to celebrate the wheat harvest.

Infirmary – the monastery's hospital.

Lollard – a pre-Protestant movement that started in about 1370. Lollards questioned the authority of the Pope and the wealth of the church. Lollards were sometimes burned as heretics.

Mappa Mundi – a very famous early mediaeval map, made about 1300. It is currently housed at Hereford Cathedral.

Misericord – a ledge on the underside of a hinged seat in a choir stall. When the seat is turned up, this ledge gives support to someone standing.

Neeps – turnips.

Peasant's Revolt – a major uprising across large parts of England in 1381 caused by high taxes and political tensions following the Black Death and the Hundred Years War in France. The rebels also wanted an end to serfdom and the removal of the King's corrupt senior officials.

Reredorter (literally, 'behind the dormitory') – a latrine. This was a building with a stream running around the outside of the walls, with wooden seats placed over the water as a very early 'flushing toilet'.

Obedientiary – an office holder within the monastery.

Prior – the second in command at an abbey.

Scriptorium – (literally, the 'writing room') where manuscripts would have been copied and office work done.

Tisane – a herbal tea.

Wind-eye – a window. In ordinary homes these were unglazed, with wooden shutters, or maybe panelled with thin sheets of horn. Only the abbey or rich houses would have had glass.

Illustrator's note

All the illustrations are based on actual mediaeval manuscripts.

Glastonbury Abbey as Brother Bernard knew it in 1408

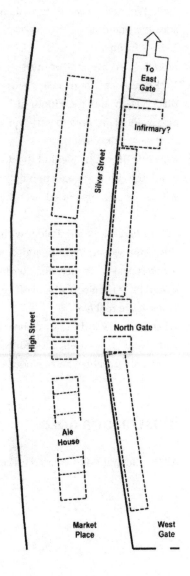

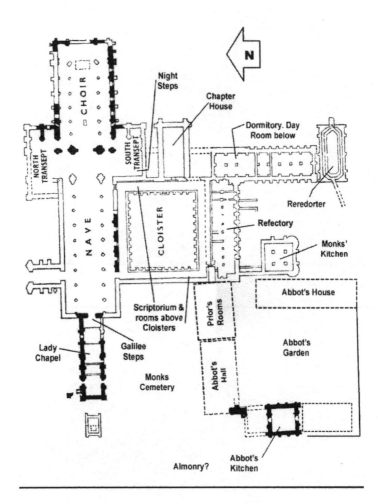

N

CHOIR

NORTH TRANSEPT

SOUTH TRANSEPT

Night Steps

Chapter House

Dormitory. Day Room below

Reredorter

NAVE

CLOISTER

Refectory

Monks' Kitchen

Scriptorium & rooms above Cloisters

Prior's Rooms

Abbot's House

Lady Chapel

Galilee Steps

Monks Cemetery

Abbot's Hall

Abbot's Garden

Abbot's Kitchen

Almonry?

Broken Angels is based on a true story

By the early fifteenth century, Glastonbury Abbey, one of the wealthiest and most important monasteries in Britain, had become a hotbed of gossip and rumour. There were tales of internal feuds and lax discipline, illicit sex, and several questionable 'business' deals. Even worse, there were numerous complaints about the abbot, John Chinnock.

At last, King Henry IV and the Church hierarchy decided to act. In September 1408, the Archbishop of Canterbury, Thomas Arundel, visited Glastonbury with an entourage of influential men to resolve the situation.

The archbishop's visitation report still exists[1], but it's mostly a list of punishments meted out, not the actual crimes. 'Broken Angels' uses that report and many of the people mentioned in it, to imagine what was going on.

Our story will take you back six hundred years to a time that's often over-spiritualised and romanticised, but in reality was cruel and brutal, especially for the ordinary working people.

Beth Webb and Mark Hutchinson 2020

---

[1] Translated from the original Latin by Sir H. C. Maxell-Lyte and M. C. B. Dawes in *The Register of Thomas Beckyngton* (Somerset Record Society, volumes 49 and 50, 1934). Pages 550-557

X

The Spy

It was a wet September evening, in the year of Our Lord 1408, and my master, Thomas Arundel, by Divine Providence Lord Archbishop of Canterbury, summoned me to attend him. We'd only arrived at Glastonbury Abbey a few hours before, so the messenger escorted me through the unfamiliar warren of barely-lit stone corridors and courtyards. He indicated a heavy wooden door and left.

I knocked.

'Come.'

Lifting the latch, I entered the apartment, lit by a real wax candle and sumptuous enough for King Henry himself – the walls hung with tapestries and the bed was curtained in crimson damask. The wind-eye stood open, letting a breeze stir the fabrics and admitting moths to dance around the flickering flame.

Unlike most men, my master lost none of his authority without his robes. He sat, straight-backed, reading a parchment at the table. He looked up as I entered. In the yellow light, his hands and face seemed starkly pale against his simple black habit. His mouth twitched in what may have been a smile. 'Ah, Brother Bernard. Thank you for coming. Please sit. Will you take some wine?' He indicated a jug and two pewter cups.

'Thank you, Your Grace.' I poured for us both, and sat. My master drained his cup, stared at me over its rim, then proffered it. 'See this?' he asked.

'Yes, My Lord.' I rose to refill it, but he held up a hand.

'No more. This cup wants to tell us a story. Do you know what it wishes to say?'

Bemused, I blinked. 'How do you mean, Your Grace?'

He sighed. 'Can you tell what this cup has been used for?' The archbishop tipped it upside down and a single drop of red glinted in the candlelight, then fell, staining the wood. 'What has this cup *held*?'

'Wine.'

'How do you know?'

'By examining the residue – as you have just demonstrated.'

The archbishop leaned back in his chair. 'So, you believe the witness of your own eyes? That is reasonable. But if you *asked* this cup what it had held, how would it answer you?'

'Er, it would not, my Lord.' I shifted uneasily on my chair. Was the archbishop drunk, or in a fever? His voice sounded steady; he wasn't slurring.

My master nodded. 'Well answered, Brother Bernard. Now, I wish you to interrogate all the cups in this monastery.'

I opened my mouth, then shut it again. Whatever I said would sound foolish, for I had surely missed the archbishop's point. Seeing my confusion, he pushed my wine toward me. 'Drink up. Tell me, why do you think you are here?'

'Scribing for your examination of the abbot, the prior and the monks of Glastonbury,' I replied. 'To assist Your Grace in your investigation as to why the abbey has fallen into ill-repute. I have my ink mixed and plenty of quills and parchment.'

2

'Scribing?' He waved his hand dismissively. 'Any fool can do that. What I really want you to do is much more important.' He leaned forward and stared at me, his eyes glistening in the candle flame. 'I need you to ease the tongues of the servants and lay brothers with wine. Go into the taverns and buy ale for the washerwomen, listen to their tales of the monks.'

I thought he was jesting and I smiled.

But his gaze held no mirth. 'Will you do it?'

I gaped. Was my master having a brain-fit? 'But that's *gossip*, My Lord, strictly forbidden by Holy Writ...'

He shook his head. 'Only when the intent is malicious. In this case, my son, you will be, as it were, my wine taster, discovering what has turned Christ's wine sour. You are to examine the abbey's dregs and find out what's *really* going on. What demons are at work? Is it witchcraft or a simpler sin? Has the abbey lost sight of its Holy Vocation; does it now stand in need of spiritual refreshment?' He pulled a piece of bread from a loaf by his elbow and wiped it around the inside of the cup. 'If I ask Abbot Chinnock or Prior Coffyn what is happening here, they will tell me exactly what they think I *want* to hear. To continue our metaphor, I will be offered the finest wines because I am their archbishop and their guest. What I need is someone to wipe the bottoms of the cups and discover the truth of what is *really* infecting this once-magnificent house of God.'

He poked a finger toward me. 'And you, my fine young Oxford graduate, have been chosen for that task; to be my ears and eyes.'

I drained my wine and swallowed hard.

3

I was a Master of Theology, the archbishop had hinted I could possibly join his staff... *Now* I was reduced to buying ale for harlots in the back streets of Glastonbury! What had I done to offend him? Was I being punished for some unconscious sin?

My cheeks burned. I clenched my fists. This was insufferable. Intolerable. What an insult... I... I...

Then I stopped and thought. Maybe I was being tested to see if I'd fall into temptation, or to discover how obedient I'd be? I took a deep breath. 'I understand, Your Grace, very wise,' I muttered through clenched teeth. 'May I be excused?'

'Of course. You need to get started straight away – tonight if possible. But don't linger in the taverns, get some rest too, for I expect to see you at matins. You and I must set an example to the brethren of this house who've been led astray by sloth and lax ways.'

'I am honoured to serve, Your Grace.' I stood to take my leave.

'Wait! You'll need this – for expenses.' He pushed a clinking bag of coins across the table.

'Thank you, My Lord.' I hung the purse from my belt and bowed. The archbishop turned back to his documents and I left, leaving the moths to their frenzied candle dance.

Outside the door, I hesitated, trying to recall whether to turn left or right down the rush-lit corridor. Inside my head I was still raging with fury at my degradation, but I tempered my steps as I found the cloister and crossed the day room. Then throwing decorum aside, I ran to the latrines in the reredorter. Saints be praised, it was empty, but the place stank of stale piss. A couple of oily rush-lights had been stuck at angles into a lump of clay and shimmered in the chilly blackness. I chose a wooden seat that seemed relatively clean, and there I sat, the stream's flowing draft cooling me down below while my head steamed with fury.

Before we left Canterbury, the archbishop said he'd chosen me as his assistant for my skill, accuracy at note-taking, and my keen eye for detail. And now he was treating me like dross! Why didn't he get his groom or one of the lay brothers to do his dirty work?

I finished my business, grabbed a wiping-sponge from the jug of vinegar and shuddered at the dead, white worms that clung to it. I pulled a wad of dried grass from my pouch and used that to wipe myself clean.

Worms! That was what this was really about. Glastonbury Abbey, once so grand and important it was drawn on the Mappa Mundi, was now infested with demons crawling about like arse worms, wriggling in and out, contaminating everything. And *I'd* been sent to buy them drink and 'make friends'! By God's breath, what had I done to deserve this? I was being abused unjustly!

I went to the bucket and washed my hands and face. I had to obey. I was sworn to do so, but sweet Mother Mary, why me?

As I dried myself, a thought struck me. Our Lord had eaten and drunk with whores and sinners. I took a deep breath. I must humble myself to do the same!

Just as I was about to leave, I heard a frenzied spluttering and splashing. I plucked a spare tallow strip from the table, lit it, and peered down one of the holes in the latrine bench.

Startled eyes stared up at me from the stream-bed below. I pushed the seat-plank aside, reached down and grabbed the man's arm, dragging him out like a new-born babe into the world, dripping wet and stark naked.

Once plucked fully from the drains into the reredorter, the man danced around, covering his crotch and shivering. 'Thanks! By St Loy, that water's icy tonight!' He dived under the table in the centre of the chamber and scrambled in the shadows. He reappeared with his habit and breeks, shook them out and pulled them on. 'I haven't missed vespers and compline, have I?'

'Vespers and compline? No, you've got at least twenty-two hours to go,' I replied tersely.

His face lit up as he tied his shoes. 'I get it, twenty-two hours! Ha! Nice one!' He buckled his belt, ran his fingers through his tonsured hair and held out his hand with a cheery, three-toothed grin. 'You're new? I'm Brother Richard.'

'Brother Bernard,' I replied, shaking the chilly fingers.

'Where are you from?' Richard asked. 'I heard someone might be coming up from Wellington Priory this week.'

'I'm with the archbishop's inquiry team,' I replied.

Brother Richard froze. I saw my chance. I had to begin somewhere. 'But I'm feeling a bit lost and out of my depth. I only left university a few weeks ago and got plunged straight into all this,' I grinned sheepishly. 'I – suppose you don't fancy coming out for a flagon of ale, do you? My treat, I've got money.'

Brother Richard eyed me suspiciously.

I jangled the purse at my belt. 'I was given this to look after. A couple of coins won't be missed.' I winked.

Richard's face broke into another smile and he slapped me on the back. 'By Heaven's bells, you're on! C'mon,' and he turned back to the hole from which he'd crawled.

I gulped. 'Can we – er get out through a gate or something?' I nodded toward the latrines. 'I don't fancy, you know, going that way.'

'I'm just tidying up, can't have anyone guessing my secret,' he chuckled, pushing the plank seat back into place. 'I only take that route to impress Berthe, my young lady. I like her to think I have to go through endless trials and tribulations to get to her. It also means Moll, my other woman who lives just across the market square, won't see me leave the abbey and wonder why I'm not visiting her. She's the jealous sort.' He grinned.

I gasped. 'You have *two women*, and you go visiting one naked and wet?'

He shrugged. 'Berthe likes the naked part, and the wet isn't too bad as long as I use the seat at the top of the latrines where the stream comes *in*. The other way isn't so pleasant.' His eyes sparkled mischievously.

'I can imagine,' I replied, following him through the day room, where several brothers sat chatting by rush-light.

Ignoring them, we walked around the cloister and took a short cut through the church. I slowed in the nave to bow, restoring my sense of worship and devotion before the richly coloured statues. The altar candles scented the air with honey, mingling with traces of incense. I breathed deeply to calm my soul. 'Hail Mary, full of grace,' I prayed, 'protect me, your undeserving son, as I descend into hell tonight. Send angels to guard me from the demons that lurk in wait.'

Then I ran after my guide through the north door.

We found ourselves in the outer courtyard. The night was getting chilly as we strode the cobbles between the workshops and offices. Ahead, a dark stone gatehouse towered over us; at its base, a brazier burned.

'Will the gates be locked?' I asked.

My friend leaned close and whispered, 'Only to those who have no money. Come, or the ale will be sold out.'

As we neared the fire, a heavily-built man emerged from the shadows and stepped in front of us, arms folded. His fire-lit face was pock marked and ugly. He neither moved, nor spoke.

Brother Richard coughed and nudged me hard.

'Oh, yes.' I took a small coin from the archbishop's purse and held it out.

The man scowled. 'It's been clipped.'

I gave him another. He nodded and opened a narrow door in the heavy wooden gate. 'Have a good evening, brothers,' he growled.

We found ourselves outside the abbey in a muddy

street. We turned left and downhill toward the market cross where another brazier burned and half a dozen watchmen stood in the golden light, their arms wrapped around young ladies.

On seeing us, a skinny girl wriggled free, jumped up and ran to my companion. She flung her arms around his neck and kissed him full on the lips. 'Richard!' she exclaimed, 'I thought you weren't coming tonight. How did you get away?' Noticing me, her eyes glinted and her cheeks dimpled. 'Who's your friend?' she purred. 'He's a good-looking lad. I'd like to get acquainted.'

'This is Brother Bernard,' Richard replied, 'Now Moll, my sweet, you're *mine*, not his, so keep your eyes to yourself, wench! Let's go to the inn; it's starting to rain again.'

Martha

The alehouse was a low stone hall with a mangey thatched roof. Inside, it was noisy, squashed, and stank of farts and armpits. The fire made the air too hot, despite the wind-eye shutters being flung wide. Richard called over a barmaid, slapped her arse and demanded ale. 'He's paying,' he said, jabbing his thumb in my direction.

The girl was grey-faced even in the ruddy firelight. She held out her hand. I duly produced another coin. She closed her fingers around mine and held on. Looking up at me with a black-toothed smile and stinking breath, she asked, 'Will there be anything else tonight, Sir?'

I tugged my hand free. 'No, there won't!' I snapped.

Her face fell as she turned to fill three tankards from the nearest barrel. I felt a twinge of guilt for being so terse. I followed and stooped down beside her. 'What's your name?'

'Martha, Sir.' She passed me a foaming leather tankard and started to fill the next one.

'Martha, why do you let Satan tempt you like this? The brothers are men of God, dedicated to chastity – do you know what that means?'

''Corse. I ain't stupid.' She handed me another tankard. The tap wasn't flowing so well, so she kicked the barrel. 'Do us a favour and tip it up a bit, Sir?'

'One moment…' I went back to set the pots of ale next to Brother Richard and his lass. They were talking softly. I didn't interrupt but returned to tip the barrel for Martha.

11

She didn't look at me while she knocked at the tap and tried to squeeze another draught from the keg. 'Us girls – well, we ain't tempted, Sir, not like you mean. You see, we're just hungry.'

I was distracted by the stinking sludge she was pouring into my ale pot. 'Hey!' I protested, 'I'm not paying for this puke!'

By the meagre light, Martha upended the pot onto the already soggy straw floor and yelled over her shoulder, 'Martin! This one's done. Get us another, there's thirsty customers waiting!'

A bent man with a filthy apron hobbled to our side, lifted the barrel as if it were a baby, rolled it through the room, knocking at people's ankles without apology, then shoved it in a corner before disappearing through the crowd.

'What do you mean, 'hungry?' I demanded, returning to our conversation. Martha shrugged and wiped her face on her apron. 'Most of us are good girls, we don't want to sin, but what're we to do? We all got babies and grannies at home, all wailing for food and firewood.'

I was shocked. 'Then your husbands must provide for you.'

The girl's eyes welled with tears. 'My Hugh were a good bloke, but he got caught under a cartwheel last Lammastide. Broke his back. He died in agony three days later. I spent all our savings burying him proper.'

'Oh… I'm sorry. But surely the abbey gives you alms?'

She shrugged. 'Yes – but it's never enough and to get a bit more, we have to offer – *favours*, if you get my meaning,

Sir.' She looked at me, wide-eyed. I sensed she was telling the truth.

'Is that what Brother Richard is doing?' I asked. Does he pay for favours?'

'Sometimes. But mostly he's just lonely. He joined the monastery to get away from his wife; she were a scold like you wouldn't believe. Richard's a good sort. When he can, he brings us white bread and cheese or herbs for the pox.'

A low rumbling and a parting in the crowd announced Martin returning with a fresh barrel. I helped him settle it into the cradle.

Martin knocked out the bung and shoved in a tap. The ale gushed and foamed, Martha filled my pot and I gave her an extra coin. 'That's for your children,' I said.

Her eyes widened. 'You changed your mind? D'yer want to come out back?' she asked, lifting her skirt a little.

'No, thank you, Martha. Just pray for me, if you have a moment.'

Bad Ale

When I returned to the table where Brother Richard had been sitting, the bench was empty. I sat leaning against the whitewashed wall and closed my eyes to absorb what Martha had said, and at the same time trying to unobtrusively eavesdrop on other conversations nearby. I needed to know if Martha was alone in her troubles, or if her story was common.

As I listened, I recognised the voices of Richard and his woman drifting in through the open wind-eye. They were out taking the night air, despite the rain. I wondered if Richard's mother might have been a duck, as he obviously held no dread of getting wet.

I listened hard.

'If he don't want any, what's he doing here?' Moll demanded crossly. 'Holy men aren't good for business. They put the regulars off their usual. Can't you get him back to the abbey?'

I heard piss splashing against the wall as Brother Richard replied. 'Can't, my little honeycomb. He's with the archbishop's lot. He's a spy, I'd bet my salvation on it. He wants to know everything, *and* he's got a purse full of silver pieces to pay for it. I don't trust him one inch, but because of him I got the chance to come and squeeze the breast feathers on my favourite pigeon, so he can't be all bad! C'm'ere…'

'Oh! Stop it! You are naughty!' the girl squealed.

I swallowed my drink; it tasted sour. I wiped my mouth

14

on my sleeve and left the tavern. Walking in the opposite direction from my new 'friends,' I chose a narrow alley between the shops and stalls and found my way back to the abbey gate. I knocked and the same grim-looking porter opened the door and held out his hand. 'I paid you before,' I protested.

He scowled. 'Don't remember.'

Too tired to argue, I paid up.

Once inside, I staggered across the courtyard. My head span, that ale was making my belly churn. I hoped I wasn't going to throw up. I needed sleep. Matins was only three hours away and the archbishop would be watching out for me.

The great bell was striking eleven as I entered the church. Despite my nausea, I wished I could watch the clock automata, but it was too dark. When we had arrived that afternoon, I'd been fascinated by the display of St Michael slaying the devil at the striking of the hour – a magnificent piece of machinery operated by a fine balance of weights and pulleys.

The thought of St Michael assured me that all would be well, for the devil could never win. I crossed the chancel, bowing before the saints once more, but this time I paused to pray for Martha and her fatherless children. I hadn't asked how many she had, or how old. I should have given her two coins. But it was too late. I wasn't going back. I climbed the night stair and entered the dormitory where three oil lamps set into glass lanterns sent pale light dancing down the wooden partitions. As I found my pallet near the end of the hall, I noted a few beds were empty, but books and blankets were left in dishevelled heaps, so they had occupants, but they were otherwise engaged. I wondered which one was Richard's. No obedientiary sat at the door counting the brothers in.

What was the prior doing? Did he not care for the discipline that would save the brothers' souls? I had no strength for anger; I just needed sleep. I found my cubicle, the third from the end, and knelt to pray. But I couldn't concentrate. Not only did my belly and head ache, but painful groans came from the next cubicle. I peered over the partition, I was a long way from the nearest lamp, but in the near darkness, I could just make out a very large monk who lay grunting and thrashing.

'Brother, do you need the infirmarian?' I asked softly.

He froze, gasped, and split into two thin figures who leapt off the bed and disappeared into the dark.

Sighing, I lay down, pulled the blankets under my chin and closed my eyes. I was too ill to care.

Demons

The clock struck two. The night was pitch black, only two oil lamps still struggled to burn. A young novice carrying a lit taper came tapping the end of each bed, calling the occupants by name. 'Arise with joy,' he urged. 'Time for matins, Brother'. Very few of the men bothered to stir, let alone be joyful. Most swore and one threw a shoe at the boy.

I yawned and wrapped myself in my cloak, for the night had turned chilly. As I groped through the dark dormitory toward the night stair, I stumbled, and the world span.

Gagging and retching, I ran for the reredorter, making it just in time, emptying both ends of my guts into the nearest latrine. Ill as I was, I couldn't help chuckling at the thought that Brother Richard might be lurking somewhere below.

Feeling better, I spat, washed, and re-joined the brothers lining up in the cloister. The windows that over-looked the quadrangle were not glazed, so the wind and rain found us, soaking our robes and feet. Despite the cold and wet, I was sweating – flushing hot and cold in turn. My belly still churned and my head throbbed. I was struggling to stay upright.

All around me, the monks chattered and gossiped incessantly from under their hoods. Every word felt like a hammer to my aching ears.

'Silence!' roared a gravelly voice, probably one of the sub-priors.

Quiet fell, then someone farted. The others guffawed

like schoolboys. Before the sub-prior could yell again, the church doors swung open, golden candlelight spilled across the wet paving, and we processed into the House of God, where the rain, like the devil, was shut firmly out.

Or so I hoped.

On the altar, twenty or so beeswax candles flickered in the draught, casting warmth and light on the gilded statues of the abbey's patrons, St Peter and St Paul. The air smelled of honey and incense. I began to relax, for surely such noble saints would never permit the devil to contaminate this holy place they guarded for Christ.

I took my place in the choir, the cantor chose a note, and we launched into the first psalm.

I felt too unwell to sing. Resting my rear on the misericord, I straightened and considered my brothers. The archbishop had told me our God-given mission was to root out the evil that lurked in these men's souls, shaming the name of Holy Mother Church. I had been honoured to be part of such a crusade, but maybe that pride was the sin for which I was being punished?

Now I was here, I had a job to do. I resolved see to it with all humility.

But I was distracted. Despite the rise and fall of the heavenly chant, I couldn't get Martha out of my head. She'd made me think. Were demons really lurking or were well-meaning men and women simply too weak and needy to fight temptation? Dare I believe so? I had to think and be logical, as Plato would have demanded.

Denying my aching head and belly, I looked about me, searching for tell-tale marks of Satan on those nearby.

I could hardly see the men's faces, but I knew a few by the way they stood: the abbot of course, tall, scrawny and forever scratching at lice. Brother Cellarer, fat as butter, the belt around his waist scarcely meeting over his belly... Then I gasped, for glaring at me from across the choir was Brother John Polglas.

It was he who had stirred the pot last summer by reporting the abbot and causing this investigation. But was he friend or fiend? He had done the right thing by reporting the devil's workmanship, but what was *he* getting out of it all? He must want or need something badly to have taken such a step? Some sort of office or preferment, maybe? Or was he hoping for bribes to get him to shut up? Men rarely did good deeds simply for the Glory of God. I didn't like the way Brother Polglas glared at me in the candlelight. He had a cross-eyed squint, a sure sign he was demon-spawn, or so my mother always said. I'd have to watch him.

My thoughts were interrupted by an anthem, exquisitely begun by the boys' choir. Father Walter led us in the 'Our Father,' raising his hands to bless us.

Suddenly, I was overwhelmed with heat; my face and hands dripped with sweat. How could Hell come so near when men were at prayer? I could hardly breathe. I thought I was going to pass out.

Then Christ in his mercy restored me with cold. Shivering was a relief, but slowly the chill increased to an aching freeze gnawing at my bones. Was this the bitter chill of Purgatory? All around me, the church shifted and swayed. I forced myself to stand and concentrate on the

responses. In my heart, I knew that God was testing me, and prayer was the answer.

I heard a fluttering above my head and looked up. Small black bat-shapes were swooping through the vaulted stone arches. My heart sank, for they grew and grew as I watched.

Diving low over my head.

Red eyes glaring.

Sharp teeth bit and tore at my flesh, ripping out my precious soul!

'Begone, foul demons!' I muttered, mouth dry, hands shaking.

I tried to swat the cruel beasts away, but on and on they came, a swarming crowd of restless soul-eaters. I prayed urgently.

The brothers at my side nudged me hard, hissing at me

to be quiet, but they too shape-shifted into haggard fiends, rotting flesh hanging from their skulls, bony claws reaching toward me.

'*Sancte Michael,*

defende nos in proelio…'

But St Michael neither heard nor defended me. Instead, my stomach knotted, I spat bile and crumpled to the floor.

As the brothers filed out at the end of the service, I was left in a pounding, twisted heap, caught between the choir stalls.

At last, I was vaguely aware of a light. A figure with a candle was leaning over me and speaking. It was the archbishop. I couldn't stand, or even bow. 'I told you to loosen the tongues of the gossips, not over-imbibe yourself,' he said sternly. 'I expected better of you, Brother Bernard. Get up. Pull yourself together. I need a report of your findings before terce.'

Another shadow joined the first. A gentle hand felt my forehead. A kinder voice added, 'I believe, my Lord, that this young brother has an ague of the humours, rather than too much ale. With your permission, I'll take him to the infirmary.'

'As you wish.' And the first shadow moved back.

Arms around my back eased me upright, but my knees felt too weak to take my own weight. I sagged. A second pair of hands took my arm and somehow, I walked.

'Sleep if you must,' I heard the archbishop say, 'but don't forget your duties to Christ come first. Discipline yourself, my son. Illness is merely weakness of spirit.'

His voice was too close and too far away all at once.

Heat swallowed me, demons dressed as ten or twelve copies of the archbishop hopped and skipped around my head.

And I passed out.

Brother Nicholas

When I woke, a handful of rush-lights were burning, two or three at a time, stuck in lumps of clay on a table as in the dormitory. I could just make out a shadowy wooden room with beds along one wall and shelves laden with herbs and bottles on the far side. The air smelled of piss and vomit. To my right there were two or three beds with occupants snoring like pigs, while a short, thin, man moved amongst them, checking their wellbeing.

When he came to me, he touched my hot head. 'You have quite a fever, friend.' He took a rag from a bowl of water, wrung it out and placed it on my brow. The cooling was heavenly.

The man helped me sit and offered a small cup with a spout. 'You must drink something,' he said kindly, pressing the cup to my lips and tipping it. A tisane of chamomile cleansed away the foul taste of bitter bile. I swallowed and drank it all. Sighing, I lay back.

'I'm Brother Nicholas of Frome,' the man told me gently. 'I'm normally the almoner, but the infirmarian is away, so I'm tending his little flock of sick sheep as well as my own. Rest now. I think you've eaten or drunk something that had an evil spirit lurking inside.'

'Bad ale,' I groaned. 'I drank at the tavern in the market place.'

My nurse nodded. 'Not wise, it's best to stay in the safety of these walls and not wander out. God's protection is always kind, but those who stray may be punished a

little for their misdemeanour.' He smiled warmly.

I closed my eyes and didn't answer – I didn't have the energy to explain, and it was probably best to keep the archbishop's mission secret. Even though he was mistaken, Brother Nicholas was gentle in his rebuke. I believed he was a good man I could trust. He spoke again, but I could not make out his words as sleep claimed me.

When I woke a second time, daylight filtered in through

the horn wind-eyes along the walls. Seeing another cup by the side of my bed, I drank, swung my feet to the floor and stood. This time the world did not shift and sway. Seeing a bucket under the truckle bed, I relieved myself, then finding my habit folded on a chair, I dressed.

I sat and rubbed my face, trying to collect my thoughts, but as I did so, a troupe of boys from the abbey school bounced in through the door and gathered round the table. 'What's for breakfast?' one demanded.

Another lifted the lid of an iron pot and inspected the contents. 'Pottage with honey, lucky sods,' one exclaimed, while another raided a plate of sliced boiled fowl and bread.

'Wish there was mustard,' he complained through a stuffed face.

One of his companions laughed. 'You'll neither see mustard nor four-footed meat this side of becoming abbot, Hal Glover! So shut your face and take what you can without complaining!'

At that moment, Brother Nicholas came in through the far door of the room, carrying a pitcher of milk. Glaring, he put his burden down and clapped loudly. 'Away with you! Thieves and scoundrels, the lot of you!' He grabbed a broom and swung it around. Some he caught on the shin or arm, but they didn't care.

The boys shoved what they could into their pockets and darted past the almoner making long noses at him. Then they bounded out of reach like young frogs and skedaddled toward the door.

'Just wait until I tell the abbot,' Nicholas roared.

25

'He won't care, he's never bloody here, is he?' Hal retorted.

'He is today, AND he's got the Archbishop of Canterbury with him!' Nicholas replied.

'Yeah, and I'm the man in the moon,' a cheeky redhead called back. And they were gone.

Still wobbly, but with my world remaining more or less upright, I hobbled to where Brother Nicholas was trying to bring order to the breakfast chaos.

'Can I help?' I ventured.

Nicholas looked up. Now it was light, I could see him clearly, a pleasant faced, youngish man with freckles and a tonsure of sandy coloured hair. 'All sorted,' he smiled. 'Do you feel like eating?'

I shook my head. 'Just tisane, please.'

Nicholas handed me a dish of soot and a cup of salted water. 'Scrub your teeth first,' he said, 'you'll feel better with a clean mouth.'

I pulled my best twig from my pouch, brushed, swilled and spat in the bucket under my bed. Meanwhile, Nicholas poured a fragrant liquid from a large jug. 'Sit down, you're still as white as linen, friend.'

I sat and sipped at my medication. 'Why do the boys come in here and steal food?' I asked. 'Don't they get fed?'

Nicholas laughed. 'They are *boys* – they'll be hungry forever, whatever Brother Kitchener gives them. Don't you remember what it was like being twelve?'

I nodded ruefully, but I didn't want to think about food right then. I swallowed the chamomile tea and thanked Nicholas warmly.

'Father Benedict's Rule is hard on the young, much as he loved them,' Nicholas continued. 'I hope the archbishop will be kind...' He raised an enquiring eyebrow. 'I expect their unruly behaviour will be considered in this inquiry?'

I nodded. 'Probably.'

'If Brother Kitchener would give them a little more porridge and maybe some honey in the mornings, they wouldn't be so ravenous,' Nicholas continued. 'A little practical compassion goes a long way, especially with boys, that's why I'm careful how I swing my broom – I wish to remind them they shouldn't be stealing, but not exactly stopping them either.' He smiled. 'I always ask Brother Kitchener for a little more food than we really need. It wouldn't do to go short.'

I could see Nicholas' point, but sadly, I knew the archbishop would be less lenient in his judgements. 'What do you know about the women in the town?' I ventured. 'I met a widow last night; she doesn't get enough alms to feed her children. She has to offer "favours" to the monks to get extra bread. Can the abbey not help more?'

Brother Nicholas glanced around the chamber. A novice was handing round bowls of pottage to the patients.

'Let's go outside, it'll be easier to talk,' he whispered.

We sat together on a bench by the door. The sun was up, but the towering stone wall of the abbey church kept us in the shade. In the clarity of the day, the demons had left my head, but I was still unwell. I shivered.

Nicolas felt my forehead once more. 'You still have a fever, you should be in bed for at least another day.'

'I wish I could, but I dare not; the archbishop expects me

27

to keep working. Please, tell me about the women.'

'I will, but first…' The almoner went back inside, fetched a shawl, and wrapped it around my shoulders. Then folding his arms, he leaned against the wall. 'Ah, yes, the women… They are all God's children.'

I raised an eyebrow. 'So not possessed by the devil to lead good brothers astray?'

He laughed bitterly. 'No, friend. I think I may have seen the devil, and he wasn't dressed as a peasant girl, believe me!' He sighed. 'We give what we can, as the Bible and Christ himself commanded, but anything these good people manage to grow in their fields, however hungry they are, they're compelled to pay a tenth to the church. And it's the good produce they have to bring. If the harvest is bad, the peasants keep the maggot-eaten portion, the church gets the best.'

'But where's the harm?' I asked. 'Surely tithes are gathered for redistribution amongst the poor?'

'In theory, yes, but in practice most goes straight to our kitchens and the peasants get the peelings – if they're lucky.' He sighed and shook his head. 'I fear, Brother, that most abbeys – not just this one – are filled with greedy men who like to live comfortably and help themselves to the best of everything.'

I blinked. 'Why is this allowed? It is not Christ's way.'

He shrugged. 'Because they can. It has been ever thus. The women, the orphans and the sick don't have the power to stop them or a voice to complain. And the king doesn't care,' he added quietly.

'But hasn't life improved since the peasants' revolt?'

Nicholas thought for a moment, 'Yes, although I am too young to remember. But there is little compassion in the eyes of Holy Mother Church – or the law. I fear we have lost our way here at Glastonbury. Our vocation has become entangled with power and politics. Sadly, there's no real way out of poverty unless you are very clever, young – and a man.'

He looked at me squarely. I winced.

He went on, 'The women, the children and the elderly get the dregs of our "charity". Although some girls probably have fun with their patrons, that isn't always the case. I will never judge a girl for lifting her skirts to feed a child, or even herself. Disease stalks every harlot's bedchamber. These young women will soon lose their looks and have to beg. Then their miseries will really begin.'

I thought of Moll in the arms of her watchman and then Brother Richard the night before. Was a little laughter so terrible when faced with such a grim future? I hoped God would be merciful; I vowed to pray to Holy Mary Magdalene for their redemption.

'However,' Nicholas interrupted my thoughts, 'if you have the archbishop's ear, please tell him this: the monks – Brother Richard included – take cruel advantage of the women. It is our Christian duty to give bread, herbs and pennies to those who cannot repay. Our Lord said, "It is more blessed to give than receive". Women and girls should not be compelled to bend too low over the washing barrel to earn enough to live.' He placed a hand on my shoulder and looked me in the eye. 'This "trade" must break Our Lady's heart.'

Just then, the abbey clock struck a quarter hour.

'What time is it?' I asked.

'Prime is over, the sun rose half an hour ago.'

I stood and handed back the shawl. 'Thank you for your care and for explaining things, Brother, but the archbishop doesn't approve of his staff being ill. I won't neglect to explain your insights.' I poured the last of the coins from my purse into Nicholas' hands. 'From the archbishop, for your work with the poor,' I said.

Without that money, I'd have to manage on my wits from now on – but in my heart I knew I'd spent it more wisely than on a whole barrel of poisonous ale.

As I made my way to the scriptorium above the eastern arm of the cloister, I wondered briefly whether my friend the almoner might be leaning toward Lollardry. I was loath to betray him, for Nicholas of Frome was the first truly Christ-like man I had met for a long time.

Or… was Nicholas the voice of the Devil in his most cunning of disguises – blaming poor, misled monks rather than the evil, sinful whores? I wished my head did not ache, for I could not think.

Brother Polglas

Reaching the scriptorium, I was relieved to see it was empty. On both sides were wind-eyes set with clear glass, admitting good light for every desk. I chose one about halfway down the eastern wall to avoid the direct sunlight on my work. In my befuddled state, I'd neglected to gather my bag with parchment, ink, quills and sand from the dormitory. There were communal supplies up here, of course, but I preferred my own.

As I turned to go, Brother John Polglas entered, a ruddy-faced man with a steady stride. I stepped back to let him pass, caught my foot on a stool and went flying.

Brother Polglas glanced down and said, 'Still drunk? I thought you'd have sobered up from your little episode at matins.' His voice was flat, neither mocking nor malicious.

I struggled to my feet and watched as he walked on and settled himself at the very desk I had chosen. I had no right to complain, I was the visitor, after all, but the man's… not exactly *coldness*, but matter-of-factness and lack of assistance stirred my ire. He had not reacted to my perceived drunkenness or to the fact I had fallen and may need help. After the warmth and concern of Brother Nicholas, the cunning of Brother Richard, the grief and anxiety of Martha, Brother Polglas seemed more like a speaking statue than a man.

I put aside my irritation in the cause of inquiry.

I held out my hand and introduced myself.

'I know who you are,' he said, without looking up as he

unpacked his things. 'After last night's exploit, rolling about in the choir yelling "Demons!" Father Thomas was quite ready to perform an exorcism on you – until Brother Cammell noticed you stank of ale.' Polglas put his satchel aside and considered me, head on one side. 'It's a pity, Father Thomas is rather good at exorcisms. They can be most entertaining once he gets going.'

I made a mental note to talk to Father Thomas; his information and expertise about demons might answer some of my more pressing questions as to their presence in the abbey.

Meanwhile, my fascination with Brother Polglas was growing. While he spoke, he kept staring over my shoulder. I turned once or twice to follow his gaze but saw nothing, making me nervous about who – or *what* was behind me.

Then I realised it was the man's crossed eyes that gave this illusion. His left eye, as grey as the sea, held me in an unwavering gaze. I focused on that one.

'Why did you not help me up when I fell?' I asked, narked at his lack of courtesy.

'If you required help, you should have asked,' Polglas replied, making himself comfortable on his stool. 'I did not notice any injury or blood. Was there a reason you could not get to your feet unaided?'

I gawped.

'No? Well, if you'll excuse me, I have work to do.' And he turned his attention to a fine piece of vellum on his desk. 'I have a letter to write for the abbot, so unless you have a serious question for me, I'd ask you to kindly go away and

leave me in peace.' Once more, he fixed me earnestly with his left eye. 'I expect you have work to do also?'

'I do,' I managed to say at last. 'But I left my bag in the dormitory, is there a basket of practice scraps I may borrow from?' This conversation could prove interesting, I dare not break the thread by leaving the room.

Polglas pointed the end of his quill to a large basket near the far door. 'Over there.'

I walked over to rummage around the offcuts and damaged sheets. I had precious little time to write anything presentable before terce, the archbishop would have to content himself with notes. I would copy everything out fairly later.

As I reached for a large piece of vellum, Polglas added, 'You may wish to know that you may not borrow from that basket.'

My hand froze. I turned slowly. 'What do you mean, Brother? Why may I not take from here?'

Without looking up, he replied simply, 'I did not say you may not *take*, only that you may not *borrow*, for once worked on, that piece can never be returned in the same or better condition than before, which is the best practice when one borrows anything.'

'Thank you, Brother. Then I shall *take*, with gratitude.' I smiled, for now I understood. Brother Polglas was one of those men who sees everything straight on (despite his unfortunate eyes), and every statement must always be exact, to the point, and without decoration or embellishment. I also knew that people such as he rarely lie, for to do so makes no sense to them. Far from being demon-spawn as my mother believed, this man would be well worth talking to. I just had to persuade him.

I returned to my desk, poured a little ink from the communal pot, chose a slightly bent quill, sharpened it with my knife and began work. For maybe a quarter of an hour, the only sounds were the scratch-scratch of our nibs.

Then something occurred to me. I laid my pen aside. 'Please forgive me for interrupting you, Brother Polglas,' I began, 'but I have an important question, something I am certain the archbishop would like to know the answer to.'

'How may I be of assistance?' My companion also laid his pen aside and watched me with his left eye. I ignored the one peering over my shoulder.

'I believe it was you who reported Father Abbot and Father Prior to King Henry and Archbishop Thomas?'

'It was, but His Grace must be aware of that, for I signed the letter clearly.'

'Er, that wasn't my question...' I began.

Brother Polglas rolled his eyes and reached for his quill once more. 'Then pray, do not waste my time – or yours.'

'My apologies for being unclear,' I persisted. 'I wanted to be sure I was addressing the correct person before asking...' I continued, hesitantly

'So, what is the question the archbishop would so earnestly like to be answered?'

'Why?'

John Polglas frowned. 'Please explain, what do you mean, "*Why*"?'

'Why did you do it? What motivated you?'

He shook his head. 'I'd have thought it was obvious. The truth needs to be told. Father Abbot Chinnock has surrounded himself with men who are immature, weak-minded, improvident and dishonest; furthermore, he doesn't punish offenders as he ought. As a result, people such as the prior, the sub-priors and all the obedientiaries follow his example. Discipline has broken down and the Rule of Blessed St Benedict is being openly mocked here. Will that suffice for an answer?'

Once more, I saw neither humour nor malice in his face.

I nodded, dumbstruck at the concise precision of his reply. I knew for certain I was not faced with a demon, but an uncomfortable sort of angel with wooden wings. I suspected John Polglas wouldn't know a demon if it danced naked in front of him and tried to shove a burning coal up his nose.

'Thank you for your time and help, Brother,' I replied meekly, and set about writing down the exact words he had spoken before I forgot them.

I had scarcely finished my third page of notes before the bell rang for terce. Sprinkling sand over my work, I stood and flapped it by the open wind-eye to dry, for the archbishop expected it in his hands before he entered the church door. As I rolled it carefully, Brother Polgas coughed in my ear.

I jumped, for I hadn't heard him approach. I lost my balance and almost went flying over the same stool as before.

This time Brother Polglas grabbed my arm. 'I perceive you are not drunk as I first surmised and do after all, require help.' he stated flatly.

'Thank you,' I replied. 'I drank bad ale yesterday and spent most of the night under the care of Brother Nicholas. Since then, I have been rather dizzy.'

'Ah,' Polglas replied. 'I was going to ask why you had missed nocturns and matins, but now I understand, I shall not report you.' And with that he strode away down the stairs, pausing to call back, 'But do hurry, Brother, or you shall be late for prayer, and as you are more or less upright, that would not be laudable behaviour.'

'And the archbishop is not in a very forgiving mood these days,' I added under my breath as I gathered up the hem of my habit and ran after him.

The procession was halfway into the church by the time I reached the cloister. I stuffed my writings inside the folds of my robes. Now that I was moving around, I realised Brother Nicholas had been right, I was far from well. As soon as prayers were over, I handed my notes to the archbishop and begged his indulgence to sleep a little longer.

'Brother Nicholas, the almoner who is also acting as the infirmarian, believes it best,' I added hopefully.

At that moment, someone interrupted with an urgent message, so as my master had not actually forbidden me, I took his silence as consent and went to my bed in the dormitory, rather than bothering the infirmary for accommodation again.

Plots and Pies

I slept fitfully. In the mid-afternoon, I rose to drink from the communal pitcher on the central table. As I returned to my bed, I heard low murmurings from the stairs beyond the far door.

One of the voices was a woman.

I ran to my cubicle and slid under my bed, leaving my head almost in the gangway with my blanket pulled down low so I could hear without being seen.

The speakers entered the room; the woman sounded past her first flush of youth for her voice was coarse and harsh. From under my blanket, I saw their legs sit at the central table.

'Now we're alone, where's that pie you promised me?'

I heard rustling, then the sound of eating. The smell of good meat and sweet spices assailed my nostrils; I prayed my sore belly would not grumble.

'What do you think?' the woman asked.

'It's good, better than the last one.'

'That goat was old. All I could get.'

'Tasted more like a stringy rat than goat.'

'Don't insult my cooking, or you'll get rotted corpse next time. Now, I can smuggle ten pies in with the daily laundry basket,' she announced. 'One penny each, paid in advance.'

'You'll get paid afterwards – Saints alone know what poison you'll stuff them with otherwise.'

'No. I need money to buy the ingredients.'

'Half in advance, half at the end of the week.'

As they haggled, I saw crumbs of pastry fall around the monk's feet. A dark brown rat scurried out and helped himself. I shuddered. Where there was one rat, there were usually twenty more lurking.

'Very well,' the man sighed. Coins clinked. 'Five pence now, five tomorrow if they're good.'

'And you owe me another penny for the one you've just eaten.'

'Where's your charity, woman?'

'In yer belly. One penny! NOW!'

'That was a *sample*!'

'With good meat and spices that I had to pay for.'

He sighed. One more coin clinked. 'Can't you do more than ten a day? There's a lot of hungry men in this place.'

'Master Baker says he got to keep the ovens full of bread, only space for a few pies at a time. And the girls' laundry baskets are heavy, they're bringing in enough tasty morsels for the brothers as it is.'

The man sniggered. 'Those girls are tasty morsels all right!'

The woman lowered her voice. 'And while we're on the subjects of the girls and payments, I want ten silver groats,' she demanded, 'or I tell the archbishop about your pimping. I hear he's come to ask questions.'

'Ten groats is a lot of money,' the man replied.

'Silence is expensive,' she retorted.

His voice rose nervously. 'God's truth, I haven't got it!'

'Find it! You think I won't squeal? Too good a chance to miss, with His Holiness here an' all!' She got to her feet. 'I

mean it! Now, I can't gossip all day, I must collect the linen.
Unlike you, I have an honest business to run.'

She entered the first cubical and tugged at the sheets
and blankets.

'You wouldn't dare breathe a word!' sneered the monk.
I watched his feet crossing the rush matting to stand behind
her. 'You're in this too, right up to your scrawny old neck.
Open that stinking gob of yours, and I'll make sure you'll
be the first in the ducking stool for harlotry!'

'Ha! Done that before. T'ain't so bad. Getting wet is
nothing when I got silver in me pocket and the thought of

you fasting on bread and water for a bloody month to keep me merry. I ain't stupid.' She laughed. 'If fact, I bet 'is nibs the archbishop will give me a whole gold noble for me trouble.'

'Rubbish! Excommunicate you, more likely! Anyway, the ducking stool will only be the start. What I have on *you* will get you whipped in the pillory by the hangman. You won't be able to raise a cup to your filthy lips by the time he's finished.'

He paused and added, 'Now, I might be able to find a groat or two to grease *his* palm...'

'Then you can pay *me*!' she yelled.

'Sssh! Keep your voice down, woman!'

I heard a slap. 'Ouch!' wailed the man, but the woman laughed as she moved along the room to tug at more beds. 'Bloody layabout monks sitting on your arses all day watching us peasants wrench our bones in the fields to put neeps and roast fowl on your table.'

'Go to Hell! No one'll listen to a witch like you.'

'Bastard!' Another slap.

'Tell who you damn well like,' the monk replied. 'I don't have a groat to my name, so I can't pay you, even if I wanted – which I don't!'

'So you can't pay me for pies?'

'That's different. That money comes from the brothers.'

'Aren't you supposed to be obedient or summat?' she roared. 'Do as you're told and pay up!'

The monk spat. 'Get. Out. Now.'

'When I got me washing.' She marched from cubicle to cubicle, tossing sheets and blankets this way and that.

She was getting closer. I drew in my arms and legs into a terrified knot and held my breath.

Her boots were stamping my way. 'Know what? I gonna take your grubby breeks straight to the archbishop and I'll dangle them under his nose and say, "Oi! Your Holiness, these soggy drawers got a tale to tell…" And he'll listen. I'll make damn sure he does. Just you see! You're top of my list to drop in the stinking shit, dear brother-bloody-righteous Henry-bloody-Sone. I bet you've made a fortune, high and mighty "Brother Hosteller" supplying "entertainment" for discerning guests to suit every taste.' She lowered her voice. 'Oh, and I got even *more* on you! Only last week, I heard that you and that fat scheming cellarer, what's his name? Houndsworth, you bin organising another new "business", summat a bit more lucrative than food deliveries!'

She stopped right by the foot of my bed. The muddy toe of her boot almost kicked my nose. I was sweating – from fear this time – not fever.

'Slander and the devil's lies, woman. Who'll believe a filthy doxy against a man of God?' the monk yelled.

'*Everyone!*' she sneered. 'I got witnesses.' She roared with laughter. 'And I'm gonna make damn sure the whole world knows it! I'm gonna wash your stinking sheets and drawers in quick lime, then I can laugh as your balls drop off in agony!'

I winced in horror. Here was real demon possession at last. She must have visited Hell to imagine such a torment.

The woman returned and tugged at my bed. My heart pounded. She knocked my arm as she reached down.

I bit my tongue not to shout out.

'Leave that one,' the monk shouted, 'The brother's a visitor. Only came yesterday. Strip it if you like, but there's no pay for washing clean linen.'

She swore, flung everything down, and stomped back up the dormitory. Then I heard running and a terrified scream.

This was no time for hiding – a woman's life was in danger. Even evildoers deserved a chance to repent. I kicked and wriggled to get out from my hiding place, but to no avail. I was entangled in my sheets.

By the time I was on my feet, the dormitory was empty. I looked around. There was no trace of blood on the rush matting, but foul linen and blankets were strewn left and right.

With a spinning head and shaking hands, I started to gather the laundry into a heap, but stopped as I heard more steps on the stairs. This time I didn't hide. Even if it was the washerwoman or the pimp, they had no idea they'd been spied upon, and I had every right to be in the dormitory.

But it was Brother Nicholas the almoner again. 'I heard you were still unwell. You're shaking, how are you feeling?' he asked kindly. Taking the linen from me, he placed it by the door. 'You shouldn't be doing work, not today.'

I sat on my bed and I told him all that I'd witnessed.

Nicholas listened then said, 'Ruth Taverner organises the abbey's laundry. She insists her girls bring the clean stuff in and "make the beds" for the brothers. She must be earning quite nicely for that. And as for Henry Sone – his activities are fairly common knowledge. They're both unpleasant characters and best avoided.'

'It's a shame,' he added sadly, 'Henry and I used to be friends when we were children.'

Nicholas opened his basket and presented me with a jug of chamomile and honey tisane with a chunk of plain, new bread. The loaf was soft and sweet; I had never tasted anything so good. I hadn't realised how hungry I was.

Discretion

It was almost noon by the time I'd tidied myself up, written my latest notes, and slipped into the back of the chapterhouse.

It was built with a finely vaulted roof at least as good, if not better than the one at Wells. Elegant statues of the saints painted in vivid reds, blues and greens, looked down from their niches on us mere mortals, quietly pondering our deliberations and maybe nudging us toward wisdom and victory against the Evil One.

At the end of the great room sat the archbishop on the abbot's high seat. My master wore his formal robes embroidered with gold and sewn with jewels that flashed in the light. On either side of the archbishop, many dignitaries were seated. I did not know them, but their heraldry spoke of noble lords with bloodlines close to royalty. Amongst them sat highly respected churchmen, some of whom I had met on our arrival: John Chitterne, the prebendary of Salisbury and archdeacon of all of Wiltshire, John Bathe, the canon of Salisbury and Wells, and John Kempe, a highly respected lawyer. On either side of the hall, as if seated in choir, the monks were perched on low stools. Below them, huddled near the door, stood the lay brothers.

The press of people made the chamber hot and foul, but all were listening respectfully as the archbishop read a long document describing all the faults and misdeeds the monks had apparently committed.

As a Master of Theology and the son of a knight, I exerted my right to push through the lay brothers and stand at the very front.

As the archbishop finished reading, Abbot Chinnock (still scratching at his lice) stepped forward, kissed the archbishop's ring and prostrated himself on the cold, stone floor.

The archbishop extended a hand toward him. 'Our beloved son, John Chinnock, please speak freely.'

The abbot remained still and silent, his back heaving as if he were struggling to breathe. At last, he said, 'I swear to surrender myself to the judgement, correction, punishment and decree of the archbishop with regard to my rule of the monastery.'

Or at least, I think that's what he said, but it was difficult to hear with the man's face pressed to the floor.

'Thank you, my son,' the archbishop replied. 'You may rise.'

Many in the gathering murmured and one or two voices called out, 'We didn't hear, tell him to say it again.'

'Enough for now,' the archbishop said, waving his hand dismissively. 'It has been a long morning. After we have eaten, I require all brethren to return to their normal duties. Later, I shall summon some of you into my presence, where you will be examined. I expect every man among you to speak openly and honestly.' He stood and pronounced a blessing, just as the bell rang for prayers.

I followed the brethren into the eastern arm of the cloister to wait for my master.

At last he appeared but was pressed on all sides by

monks and visitors. The archbishop was sniffing deeply at a nosegay of lavender and rosemary; the finery of the gathered company did not guarantee sweet smelling breath.

I tried, but failed, to speak and present my work. I wanted to kneel before the archbishop and apologise for my hasty scrawlings, but there was no chance. I could only thrust the rolled sheets of vellum into his hand as he passed. He neither acknowledged me, nor my act. Instead, he stuffed my work into his pouch and kept walking, all the while talking earnestly to the noble lord at his side, the bunch of fragrant herbs held carefully between them.

Once more, I felt insulted and offended, then I stopped and thought. Surely being ignored implied that I must keep a low profile and things were getting serious? For my secret mission to continue, I mustn't be seen in the archbishop's confidence. I must play the part of a lowly servant. I would have to be more discreet in future.

Crimes and Defects

After we had broken bread in the refectory, the monks returned to their daily tasks and the Inquiry to their business.

I passed several brothers, Nicholas amongst them, waiting in the cloister for their turn to be examined. I did not stop to speak, for I still had many notes to commit to parchment. On reflection, I deemed it safer not to work in the scriptorium lest anyone should overlook my writings and read my comments about them. I was still a little dizzy, so I decided to take some fresh air before beginning.

I stepped out of the refectory into the courtyard. As the day was fine and mild, I turned my feet toward the herb garden. There I followed each of the gravel paths, rubbing my fingers through the sages and thymes, avoiding the aconite, but sniffing the fennel and lovage, although that was now past its best. The place was deserted apart from an elderly lay brother hoeing weeds.

I muttered, 'Pax vobiscum,' in his general direction and turned back toward the cloister. But then I stopped and listened, for what should have been garden-silence was ruined by the yapping of dogs. I looked around, thinking maybe a local lord had permission to cross the abbey's land with his hunt, but I saw nothing.

As I returned to the cool stone walkway, someone gripped my arm tightly.

'There you are! I want words with you!'

It was Brother Nicholas, his face like a thundercloud.

I stood dumbfounded. I had thought this man a friend.

'What did you say about me to the Inquiry? *What*? I need to know,' he spat through gritted teeth.

'Nothing but good,' I assured him.

'*Liar*! I've just been banished from the abbey for "crimes, and defects". I showed you nothing but compassion and kindness. Is this how you repay me? Is it? What have I done to deserve this? My vow of stability is as precious as the Holy Chrism to me. Because of you, I've been *banished*!' He was almost in tears.

This was inconceivable. How had I failed the only man I truly respected in the whole place? I shook my head. 'I only wrote of your kindness and charity. Before Christ's throne, I swear it.'

'If you must know, it was me who told,' hissed a voice behind us. We turned and saw an elderly monk leaning on a stick and propped upright by a weary-looking novice. 'You're a bloody Lollard, Frome. God's teeth, it's about time someone spoke the truth around here.' The old man made the sign against the evil eye with two shaking fingers, and hobbled away toward the church.

Pale as milk, Brother Nicholas ran after him. 'Father Prior, wait! It's not true. Talk to me, please. Why tell lies?'

The old man cackled and looked back. 'It's no lie, and you know it. Confess it. Be a man. If it's any comfort, I'm in trouble too! I've been "retired for reasons of infirmity" … amongst other things,' he muttered sourly. 'They can't get rid of me, but at least they've shut me up! Much good may it do them!' He prodded the young man with his stick. 'Stop rushing me boy, I need a piss. Find me a bucket before I do it here, you know the reredorter is too far.'

'Yes Father Coffyn,' the boy said, and ran.

Nicholas bowed before me. 'I'm… I'm sorry Brother Bernard. I should have guessed this wasn't your doing. I over-reacted. Please forgive me. You see, I've been sent to Canterbury. When I joined the abbey, I received a dispensation to move my elderly mother to a suitable house nearby, for she has no one else to care for her. Now I must leave by the end of the week and she doesn't have the money to come too. I'll never see her again and she's not well.' His voice sounded choked, then without another word, he strode away, his shoulders shaking.

I called after him, 'I'll see if I can change His Grace's mind.'

But Nicholas had gone.

Prior Coffyn

I knew my next interview must be with Prior Coffyn. I needed no divination to guess he was a conniving schemer, but *why*?

Nicholas had told me he thought he had seen the devil, and he wasn't dressed as a peasant girl. After hearing Ruth Taverner's screeching threats, I wasn't so sure, but maybe the abbey's prior was the servant of Lucifer I'd been sent to flush out?

The cloisters were almost empty for the brothers were at their daily tasks as the archbishop had directed. I knew I should be about my writing, but I was also intrigued by the goings-on of the Inquiry. I made my way toward the chapter house doors, intending to listen and maybe even sneak in, but I was stopped by an officious man-at-arms guarding the door. He must have been from the town's militia, as I did not know him.

'State your business,' he challenged, the end of his billhook pressed in my belly.

'I'm a member of the archbishop's retinue,' I replied.

He prodded harder. 'But what's your *business*? 'Ave you bin summoned, like?'

I shook my head but held my ground.

He gave me a sharp jab. 'Then bugger off and don't bloody come back until you's sent for. Gettit?'

I got it.

It didn't take long to find Prior Coffyn's chambers, situated at the end of the abbot's hall. I climbed the stair and knocked.

A novice admitted me to a small lobby with views over the abbot's garden with its straight paths, fruit trees and grape vines. To my surprise, a dozen or so hunting hounds were lying amongst the herbs, enjoying the late afternoon sun. Dogs weren't usually allowed in monasteries, except at the farm to catch rabbits and foxes.

My thoughts were interrupted as a door opened to my left. The novice bowed. 'Father Coffyn will see you now.'

I noticed this was the second time he'd said, "Father," not "Prior" Coffyn.' So, the old man's dismissal was immediate.

I entered the chamber. It was bright and light, its wind-eyes also overlooking the garden. Tapestries, similar to those in the abbot's guestroom but older and rather moth-eaten, hung on the whitewashed walls. Thomas Coffyn was reclining on his bed, which had once been quite grand, covered and curtained with faded red damask.

The old man crooked a finger and summoned me closer. 'Name?'

'Brother Bernard Percy,' I replied.

His eyebrows shot up. 'Percy, eh? One of the earl's brood?'

'Sadly no, my lineage is a very junior branch, Father.'

'Oxford or Cambridge?' he demanded, his eyes sharp and piercing.

'Gloucester College, Oxford, Sir.'

He sank back in his pillow and closed his eyes. 'Good,

then I can probably trust you, even though you're a spy. Tell that bloody boy to sod off, will you? I want to talk to you in private.'

The door was already closing softly. We were alone.

Father Coffyn raised a yellowed hand and pointed to a desk. 'You'll find vellum and ink on the stand. I want to tell the truth. You are to take it all down *verbatim*. Not a word changed, understand?'

'Yes Father.' I found all I needed, drew the desk near to the bed and settled to my task; at last I was fulfilling my mission properly.

'I am eighty-three years of age,' he began. 'I am a Doctor of Theology – Gloucester College of course… there are no other colleges worth mentioning,' he mumbled. 'I served here at Glastonbury since 1342, Abbot Monington was in charge in those days. I liked him, the man had vision. He remodelled part of the church and extended the choir as a plea to the Almighty to end the Black Death.'

'Did it work?'

'Of course,' he snarled, adding, 'eventually,' under his breath. 'The abbot and I got on well, and he promoted me to sub-prior, then prior within ten years. I was his right-hand man. I was soon running everything, more or less, and he depended on me more and more, not only for my administration skills, but for my spiritual insights, too.

'One doesn't get to be a Doctor of Theology for counting pebbles on a path. Oh no! I knew and understood the mind of Almighty God himself.' The old man tapped the side of his nose and gave me a meaningful look. 'The Lord has revealed great truths to me by his angels. They speak to me,

53

you know, right here, in this very room.'

I glanced at him sideways. Father Coffyn's face was earnest. He believed he was telling the truth. How should I respond? I kept writing.

He fell silent; I sensed I was expected to say something. 'What sort of truths, may I ask?'

He chuckled and flapped his bony hand loosely toward the wind-eye and the abbot's hall. 'That all this should be mine, of course, and another was that the abbey will soon crumble into ruins if I'm denied my rightful title.'

I wrote again, keeping my head low.

Was this man a prophet or cursed by the moon?

'Did any of your visions come to pass, Father?' I asked as tactfully as I could.

He sat up and glared at me. 'What a thing to ask! Of *course* they did. Even His Holiness Pope Urban V commended me on my visions. I have a letter here that tells me so.' He rummaged around and held out an old sock.

I took it and spread it on my writing desk, nodded as if I could read it, then returned it with as much reverence as I could muster to the table by his bed. My heart ached with pity for the old man's lost intellect, but it happens to most of us who, by God's grace, grow old.

Father Coffyn leaned closer and whispered, 'The Pope and I were great friends; he was a Benedictine too, so that helped. But,' he sighed, 'when the idiot Chinnock was elected abbot in 1375, I *knew* it should have been me, the Voices told me so. Obviously, bribes had changed hands and favours had been called in. It's said that even King Edward had helped, but everyone knows he went barking mad after the Black Prince drowned, so no one could trust *his* judgement.

'However, the election happened and the outcome was totally against the wishes of the angels, so I went all the way to Rome to see the Pope. But dear old Urban had died five years before, and that pillock Gregory XI was rattling St Peter's Keys. He wouldn't even see me; can you believe it? *Me*, who'd had visions from Heaven itself.

Instead, I was made to sit with some spotty ruffians who called themselves the Papal Curia.

They didn't listen of course, they just brushed me aside

like a mosquito and confirmed Chinnock's appointment.'

From the corner of my eye, I could see Coffyn was watching me for my reactions, but I kept my face as straight as John Polglas might. If the old man weren't demon-possessed, he was definitely moon-struck or had a severe ague of the humours. I kept my thoughts to myself and kept writing, hoping to dissect some truth from his ramblings later.

Just then, the three o'clock bell rang for prayer. Fearing to break my companion's train of thought, I stood and recited three Hail Marys. Without rising from his bed, Father Coffyn joined in, crossing himself vigorously.

The archbishop would no doubt punish me later for missing prayers, but I would take that as it came.

Returning to my stool, I dipped my pen and asked, 'What happened when you returned home, Father?'

The old man closed his eyes and fell silent. I wondered if he'd fallen asleep, so I coughed politely.

He replied very quietly, 'I was punished for being absent without leave from my duties.' He opened his eyes and smiled. 'But that passed. I still had my visions. I did not doubt that one day, this gross insult to the will of God would be put to rights.

'Then, about a year ago, John Polglas came to see me, and what he said made so much sense, I felt I had to help him.'

I hesitated and looked up. I hadn't expected this turn in the tale. 'What did he say?'

The old man reached a shaking hand for the wine cup on his table and drank. 'Can't you guess?'

'No.'

'But you have spoken to Brother Polglas?'

'I have.'

'What's your impression?'

'He's a man who cannot lie. He's not a simpleton, he's – just different. Incapable of guile.'

'Exactly.' Father Coffyn drank again and lay back on his bed. 'Brother Polglas said what we'd all been thinking, that the abbot was lax in his discipline and has betrayed the abbey by ignoring his duty. Polglas said he'd tried to speak with the abbot, but as you've probably heard, Chinnock's always darting about on "business". When he *is* here, he's far too busy hunting or entertaining nobility to listen. Polglas knew it was time to bring Chinnock to account. He asked if I'd support him if he wrote to the archbishop and the king.'

The old man grinned; an evil look. 'Of course, I agreed – like an arrow.'

I wrote frantically, stopping only to sharpen the end of my quill.

'This was my chance to fulfil everything the Voices had promised me,' Father Coffyn went on. 'And even better, if the appeal failed, it'd be *Polglas's* head that rolled – not mine. Or so I thought,' he added miserably.

He looked up at me, his rheumy eyes spilling tears down his wrinkled cheeks. 'But now I'm to be "retired for my great age and infirmity". I'll be dumped in one of those dingy rooms above the cloister tomorrow. No views, and those poxy students running around below my window at all hours. At least I'll have a pension of sorts – ten measly marks a year. It'll keep me in firewood, I suppose,' he grumbled.

I poured the old man more wine and resumed my work.

'At first, I thought it was all going to plan,' he continued. 'The Archbishop asked for my report and I told him every last failing of Chinnock's, down to the ghastly smell of his socks.'

'Did you also tell him about your destiny to rule the abbey?' I asked, unsure how my master would receive the news that God's angels had appointed the next abbot without consulting *him*...

Father Coffyn flung his cup across the room, spraying wine like blood. 'Did I tell? Of course I did! What do you think "Retirement because of frailty *and other reasons,*" means? Eh? He thinks I made the Voices up, or I have brain frenzy! *I* who've spoken face to face with the blessed St Michael as a friend. *Insult*! *Degradation*! *Humiliation*!'

Drooling, the old man rose from his bed, hair and eyes as wild as a manic boar, he danced around, waving his arms and gurgling incoherently. Suddenly, he lunged, grabbed my habit and pulled me up from the desk. For one so old, he held me with an uncommonly firm grip.

I was about to scream 'Devil, be gone!' but then I stopped, looked, and saw – a lonely, heartbroken old man.

He wasn't possessed. Just a weary angel with wings of imaginary feathers.

At that moment, the dogs in the garden started barking and yapping again.

Letting me go, Father Coffyn hobbled across the room and pressed his nose against the glass. 'Feeding time,' he murmured. 'How I used to love to ride with the hounds. The only time the Voices stopped was when I was galloping across the marshes, splashing through mud and water, watching the ducks and herons flying...'

I peered down into the garden where a young man with a bucket was throwing bones and meat scraps to the animals.

'I didn't know hunting was allowed in the abbey?' I began.

'Who cares?' Coffyn murmured. 'I must go and walk with the dogs this afternoon; they get restless otherwise.

I can still ride, you know. Not as I used to, but it's the only time I get any peace in *here*.' He tapped his head, then swung round and glared up at me.

'What are you still doing here, you scabby sneak-up? I've told you everything, now go and tell that archbishop of yours the truth, not that he'll believe a word of it. No one ever does, except the dogs.

'I'll miss watching them running around in the gardens,' he added softly, 'P'raps when I move, they'll let me have one of the old ones who can't hunt anymore? That'd be nice. I'd like a friend who believes me.' He looked longingly out of the window and a sour rain of yellow trickled around his feet.

I grabbed the parchment with the old man's testimony and left.

As I opened the door, Father Coffyn called out, 'Mark my words Brother, unless I become abbot soon, this great house will fall into a crumbling ruin for visitors to gawp at.

It shall be so, the Voices have told me. They never lie.'

In the lobby, the nurse-novice was sitting in the chair by the window saying his rosary.

'He's all yours,' I said, as I fled downstairs. 'I think he's peed himself.'

'Not again!' The young man groaned, but I did not stop to assist him.

Whispering in Corridors

The cloister was empty apart from another guard squatting on the chapterhouse steps playing knucklebones. A heavy-looking axe leaned against the wall by his side. I decided not to disturb his recreation.

Instead, I went and knelt in the church nave to recollect my thoughts and make up for my absence from choir half an hour before. As I finished my devotions, which included a prayer for the healing and restoration of Father Coffyn's mind, I resolved to take the parchment up to the guest chamber and leave it for the archbishop to find at his leisure.

I brushed myself down and turned to leave, planning to walk through the brothers' cemetery and thence to the Abbot's hall and guest rooms.

But then, I heard whispering from the Galilee steps behind me. Hidden by the great archway pillar at the top of the stair, I listened. There's a difference between the voices of those who whisper out of respect for the sanctity of God's house and those who do so for fear of discovery.

This was certainly of the latter sort.

The first had a high, squeaky voice, he may even have sung falsetto in choir. The second sounded nasal and stuttered.

'We must make the archbishop leave or he'll ruin everything,' said number one.

'Y-you think I-I d-don't know it?' replied his friend. 'B-but it-it'll b-be easier to shift the cloisters to the m-moon than g-get r-rid of H-His H-Holiness.'

The first voice spoke so softly I could hardly hear. I risked a step nearer. 'Do you still have that half gold piece you found in the market square last Lady Day?'

'Y-yes.'

'Give it to Richard Prentyse, he knows what to do.'

There was a pause. 'In G-God's name, why p-pay that s-scoundrel a s-sodding g-groat? The f-food he c-cooks is pig's swill at b-best.'

'He has a store of alder-bark and he's willing to use it in our very good cause,' the first man replied.

'So b-bloody what?' demanded the second man. 'There are ald-der t-trees a-p-plenty d-down by the r-river.'

'God's bodykins, man! Don't you know anything? Scrapings of alder bark in our pottage will make us all vomit, and Prentyse is the only one who can get into the kitchens to do it without questions being asked.'

'I-I'm n-not p-paying to p-p-puke!' came the reply.

I struggled to suppress my laughter; this conversation was too bizarre.

'Listen, *ninnyhammer*! Do you want to get rid of the archbishop and his minions?'

'Y-you k-know I d-do.'

How many brothers did we lose in the plague?'

'N-no idea. L-lots?'

'I have no idea either, but any hint of illness amongst the brethren will send the archbishop scuttling back where he came from faster than runny shit, without him knowing anything more than he has to. All we have to do is pay up and pretend we all have a fever.'

'I-I have a f-fine b-boil I c-could m-mention in his l-lordship's p-presence?'

'Perfect. Now give me that gold piece or our little game is up.'

'Oh, v-very w-well.' I heard a rustling of clothes. I leaned forward to see what was happening, but a heavy hand landed on my shoulder.

'What you up to, bruvver, if you doesn't mind me asking?' a smelly voice sprayed all over my cheek.

I looked into the solemn face of the man-at-arms, Mr Knuckle-bones. By the look and sound of him, I guessed he may be Mr Knuckle*head* as well.

I put my fingers to my lips and whispered, 'Listen, it's not me you should be after. I work for the archbishop. The two monks on the steps below are plotting to poison everyone in the abbey, including you if you sup with us later. Arrest them. *Now!*'

The man stared down at me, then peered around the column. Raising his axe, he stepped forward. 'Wotcha doing?' he demanded loudly.

Both men squealed and ran. The guard had been well chosen, for anything he may have lacked in brain-power was more than compensated for by speed and strength.

'Their names are Father William Luyt, prior's chaplain, and Brother John Grenehurst, third prior,' Abbot Chinnock announced as the criminals were dragged into the chapterhouse.

'Why have you brought them here?' the archbishop demanded.

I stood, bowed before the assembled dignitaries and gave my testimony to what I had overheard.

A search of Brother Luyt's person bought to light a half gold noble secreted in a pouch tucked inside his breeks.

A messenger soon brought Kitchener Richard Prentyse to the hearing, along with a bag of shredded dried bark.

'We were only following Father Prior's instructions,'

Luyt explained, his weasel-eyes glinting. 'Father Coffyn feels that, saving Your Grace,' he bowed to the archbishop, 'this visitation is unhelpful and unnecessary to the abbey.'

The archbishop's eyebrows shot up. 'How so?'

Luyt and Grenehurst exchanged glances. Brother Luyt squared his shoulders and lifted his chin like a man who knew he was about to be judged, so he may as well sin as fully as he could. 'I said this inquiry is "unhelpful" because your visitation is costing us a lot of money – not that we begrudge it, my Lord, but we should be helping the poor and paying for repairs to the buildings.' He looked meaningfully at several dark patches in the chapterhouse roof. 'They are in a very sorry state, Your Grace.'

The archbishop crossed his arms and looked down his nose at Brother Luyt, who held his ground admirably. I could not have withstood such a glare from my master.

'I understand,' said the archbishop, 'but all these good lords have gone to a great deal of trouble and *expense*,' he added pointedly, 'to come and help the abbey re-discover its calling, so why, pray tell, are we "unnecessary"?'

Luyt took a deep breath and pointed straight at Abbot Chinnock. 'All that's required, my Lord, is for this usurper who lives in luxury and never lifts a finger to do God's work here, to be removed. Straight away. Once that's achieved, and a godly, caring man is sat in his place, then we can all return to our devotions and service of the Almighty.'

The chapterhouse was filled with low mutterings and shuffling of feet.

Archbishop Arundel turned to Brother Grenehurst and

stared at him hard. Eventually, he asked, 'Is this your opinion too?'

Grenehurst stepped forward and bowed. 'I-it is, my L-lord.'

The archbishop glanced around the packed chamber, 'And did you act alone in this? Was this little plot to make us all, shall we say, "unwell", was it your idea alone?'

Luyt glared at Grenehurst, signing him to say "yes", but Grenehurst was staring at the floor. 'W-we s-simply a-acted out of o-b-bedience to our master,' he said.

'Your master?'

'Y-yes, P-Prior Coffyn, for I am his third P-Prior, I obey P-Prior C-Coffyn in all th-things.'

The archbishop linked his fingers and smiled. 'When did Father Coffyn give this instruction?' he enquired.

'J-just now, S-Sir,' Luyt replied. 'I l-looked in on him in his c-chambers to see what e-errands he might have for me, and he i-informed me the v-voice of S-Saint Michael had told him what n-needed to be d-done – with the a-alder and th-that.' Then realising he may have gone too far, Grenehurst touched his heart and added, 'I am s-sworn to o-obey, my L-lord.'

'Very commendable,' the archbishop replied. 'But surely you've heard that Father Coffyn is no longer prior?'

Luyt and Grenehurst exchanged glances once more. Both men reddened as the archbishop continued, 'And therefore, no longer must be obeyed. You are both relieved of your offices, hand your keys to my secretary, Brother Bernard Percy, and you are both confined to cloister for the foreseeable future.'

The archbishop spread his hands and smiled at the gathering. 'We shall now adjourn for refreshments. When I return, I shall wish to speak to your treasurer, Brother...' He glanced down at the list of names and obedientiaries on the desk before him. 'Brother Thomas, about the abbey's accounts. Together we shall examine the monies and alms given to the poor and the allowances for the maintenance of the fabric of the buildings.'

He stared up at the dark patches under the roof for a long moment. 'For as well as this fine building, the abbot's own roof also allows God's gift of rain to amply bless those inside. I shall also be considering the amount spent on unnecessary frivolities, such as the hunting dogs that the abbot keeps in his gardens.' He scowled at the abbot. 'Their yapping kept me awake all last night.'

With that, the archbishop stood and nodded to the nobles about him. 'May I suggest, good friends, that we partake of some wine and light refreshment? Preferably *sans* alder bark.'

They all laughed dutifully and followed him toward the abbot's hall.

Vocation

Brother Luyt and Brother Grenehurst glowered viciously as they handed me their heavy iron keys. But I didn't care, the archbishop had called *me* his secretary. I had been publicly honoured. I jangled the keys and struggled not to shout and leap in the air with glee.

The disgraced monks were escorted from the chapterhouse by two men at arms. I watched the sag of their shoulders, and was saddened. Those backs had been made – like every human's – to be lifted into glory by angelic wings. Now look at them.

I wondered who William Luyt and JohncGrenehurst had been when they entered the monastery. What were their hopes and dreams? Had they, like me, wanted to serve God as a monk? Or had they been gifted, or tithed as children whether they wished it or not? What had changed Henry Sone from being Brother Nicholas' great friend into a scheming deceiver?

How could such children of hope, so filled with life, end up broken and disgraced? What would happen to them now? Would they find redemption in the archbishop's discipline, or would their souls fester and turn even more gangrenous? Was *this* what was meant by demonic possession?

Sinners though they were, my heart grieved for them.

Laying my personal celebrations aside, I went into the church to pray.

It was another wet September evening in the year of Our Lord 1408, and my master, Thomas Arundel, by Divine Providence Lord Archbishop of Canterbury, once more summoned me to attend him.

As before, I was asked to sit and offered wine. My notes were spread across the table, but this time two candles burned to give extra light to read my hurriedly scrawled script.

The archbishop tapped the nearest parchment. 'Do you swear to the truth of these writings?' he enquired.

'I swear that is what I saw and heard, Your Grace. Whether what I witnessed is true or not, I cannot say.'

'A wise answer.' He gathered up the sheets, chose a candle, and strode to the fireplace. No fire had been lit, for the evening was mild. Then, to my horror, he held out the bundle of writings, lit them and dropped them crackling and spitting onto the hearth where they curled and crumbled to black ash.

I jumped to my feet and sprang to pull them back, but he prevented me with a gesture of his hand.

'My Lord,' I protested. 'I know my writing lacked merit for style, and there were many errors of spelling, but given time I could have presented you with perfect copies – even illuminated, if you so required.'

He smiled and shook his head. 'Easy, Brother Bernard, I have not burned your labours for any malice or criticism of your work.' He continued sadly, 'I have simply decided on the punishments we shall mete out tomorrow. Those shall be recorded for posterity, but not the sins.' He returned to his chair and sat.

'B-but why?' I was almost crying for all my lost labours.

He leaned forward, hands clasped and looked at me earnestly. 'My son, you know that God has erased all our sins – including yours and mine – so we cannot keep on record what Heaven has forgotten.'

I knelt before him. 'Forgive me, Your Grace. I didn't think. Bless me and help me understand.'

He laid a hand on my head and muttered, '*Dominus vobiscum.*'

'*Et cum spiritu tuo,*' I replied and stood.

'Sit, Brother. Maybe a little more wine will ease your distress? Firstly, you must know how greatly I appreciated your pains, many of which were excruciating from the description of brother Nicholas.'

I nodded. 'I was very unwell, Your Grace. One pot of bad ale and I was ruined, but I swear I was never drunk.'

'So I understand. You worked hard, and I am now certain I can trust you for your accuracy, loyalty and discretion. For these reasons, I am appointing you as my second secretary with immediate effect. I hope this pleases you?'

'Yes indeed. Thank you very much, Your Grace.' I swallowed hard. 'But I have a few questions...'

'Go on.'

'It's Brother Nicholas – I don't think he's a Lollard. In fact, I believe him to be the best man in the abbey, someone who follows Christ with all his heart and mind.'

'I am certain you're right, Brother Bernard.'

'Then why are you banishing him to Canterbury?' I persisted. 'What has he done wrong?'

To my surprise, the archbishop laughed. 'Banished? Not at all, quite the opposite. I want to keep him under my eye and train him, for I believe he will be an excellent abbot one day – maybe the finest ever.'

'But what were his "crimes and defects"?'

The archbishop raised an eyebrow. 'Might he not have grown vain if he knew I intended to school him for preferment?'

Knowing Brother Nicolas, I did not think it likely, but did not argue. Instead, I seized the opportunity to explain about Nicholas's grief at leaving his elderly mother, but the archbishop would not be moved. 'And Our Lady lost her Son too. It is the way of those who serve Christ, my friend.'

My heart sank. I could do no more. Then a sinister thought darkened my mind. If Luyt and Grenehurst were willing to make us ill with alder bark, what else might they be capable of?

'Your Grace, do you remember the brother who began this inquiry by writing to you of his concerns? Having seen how far the monks will go, to reserve their sinful ways, I have an intuition, nothing more – that if he stays here, his life may be in danger. His name is John Polglas.

'A man like him will never be silenced,' I continued. 'Even in his coffin, he'll be watching the grave diggers to ensure the earth is cut clean and deep – and he'll give them an earful if they do it wrongly.'

The archbishop almost laughed. 'You may well be right, Brother Bernard. Men like him often inspire hatred, even though their hearts are the truest of all.' He looked at me and raised an eyebrow. 'What would you suggest?'

72

'He will not like it, for it goes against his vow of stability, but he does not deserve to die of foxglove-flavoured soup. Can he be sent to another place where his honesty will be respected?'

'I agree, for I've had similar "intuitions". Maybe the abbey at Sherbourne could use his skills.' The archbishop stood and opened the door. 'Now, it is almost time for compline, then you really must get some sleep, for tomorrow, straight after prime I shall deliver my judgements and remind the abbey of its true vocation, then we shall leave immediately. It will be a long day.'

I went to bed, my head spinning with the confirmation of my appointment. Everything I'd ever wanted was being offered to me on a plate, and I was scarcely twenty-two!

Despite my delight, my heart was not at rest. Was second secretary to the highest church office in England the best service I could give to God? This meant that my path was set for great things in the Church – and maybe politics too. I'd never want for anything; I'd live comfortably and influence the future of the land I loved.

But what was *my* true vocation?

I had come to the abbey searching for demons and indeed, I had found traces of their foul footsteps all over the place.

At the same time, I had also discovered many who longed to be angels, but whose wings had been cut and battered. Their hearts were set on Heaven, but they could not fly. They were trodden down into the mire of life.

Instead of demons, I had found humanity in its most wonderful – and ghastly forms.

My head wanted the job of second secretary, but my heart questioned whether sitting on velvet cushions and eating roast swan with the rich and powerful was what I should be doing?

Perhaps I ought to follow Brother Nicholas' example, to help the lepers and wash the feet of those in need? Maybe my calling was to be an almoner or an infirmarian?

Next day, the abbey gates were locked firmly behind us as we rode away. I guessed no amount of coin would unlock them now, without good cause.

As we followed the muddy road northeast toward Wells, I discussed my thoughts on my vocation with the archbishop.

He was not pleased to lose his new assistant so soon, so in the end, we compromised.

I would serve him and Mother Church with my quill and my mind, but on days when I was not required, I'd be free to follow the example of my father's good friend Geoffrey Chaucer, and write the stories of the people I'd met. Not to proclaim their sins, but so in the future our Lord's poor, broken angels would find mercy and help, not judgment.

Oh, and as I was now receiving a good salary, I ordered a covered wagon to bring Nicholas's mother to a convent just outside Canterbury where she lived out her days in comfort. She died a year later – held in her son's arms.

My one regret from my visit to Glastonbury Abbey was never witnessing Father Thomas perform one of his famous exorcisms, but maybe that was just as well.

About the authors

Rev Dr Mark Hutchinson

works part-time at Glastonbury Abbey, is a retired science
teacher and manager; he is also an Anglican priest.
This book comes from his research, at Exeter University,
into Glastonbury Abbey's history.

Beth Webb MA

is an author, storyteller and illustrator.
Broken Angels is her fifth historical novel.
www.bethwebb.co.uk